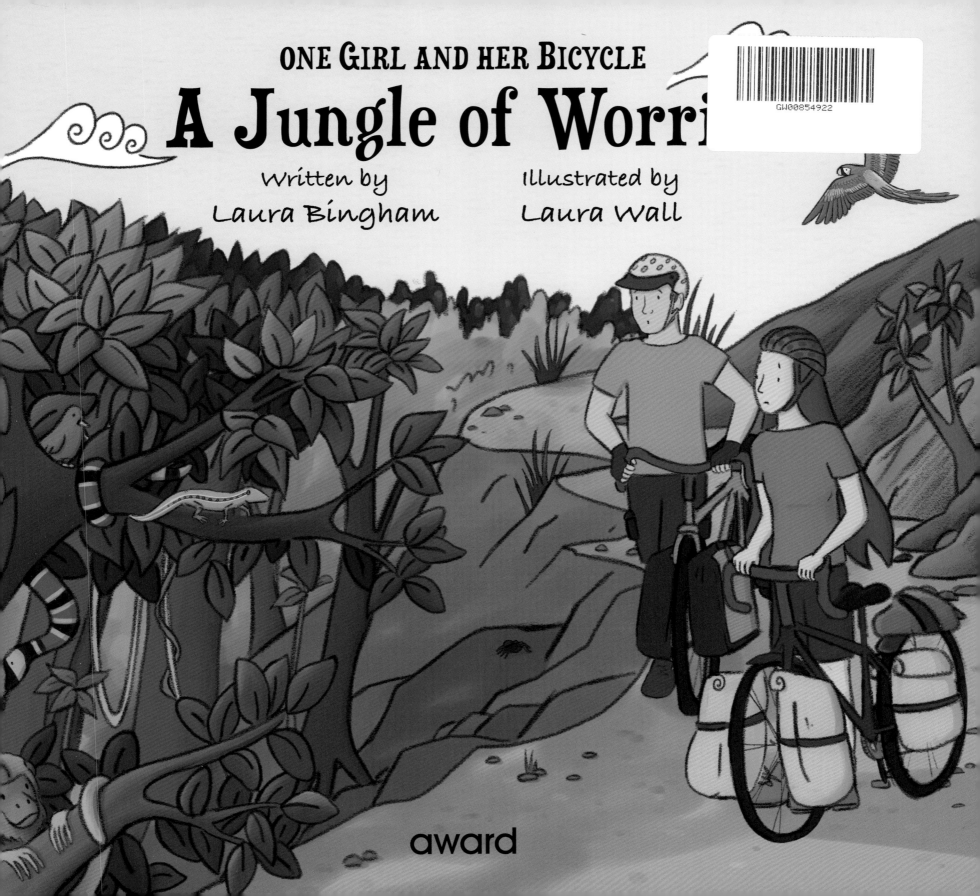

ONE GIRL AND HER BICYCLE
A Jungle of Worri

Written by
Laura Bingham

Illustrated by
Laura Wall

award

As Laura pedalled across the border out of **Ecuador** and into **Peru,** she **smiled** to herself.

She had cycled 775 kilometres, all the way through Ecuador without money, or food of her own! Only 6,500 kilometres to go!

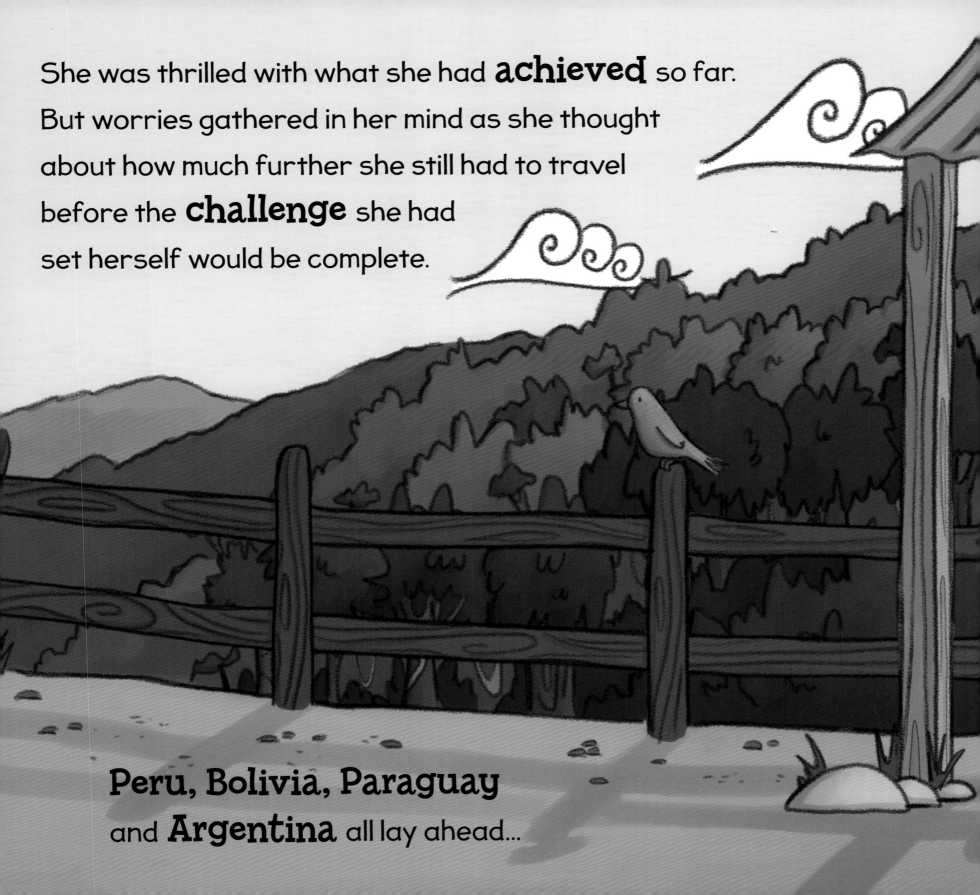

She was thrilled with what she had **achieved** so far. But worries gathered in her mind as she thought about how much further she still had to travel before the **challenge** she had set herself would be complete.

Peru, Bolivia, Paraguay and **Argentina** all lay ahead...

Peru was nearly three times **bigger** than Ecuador.

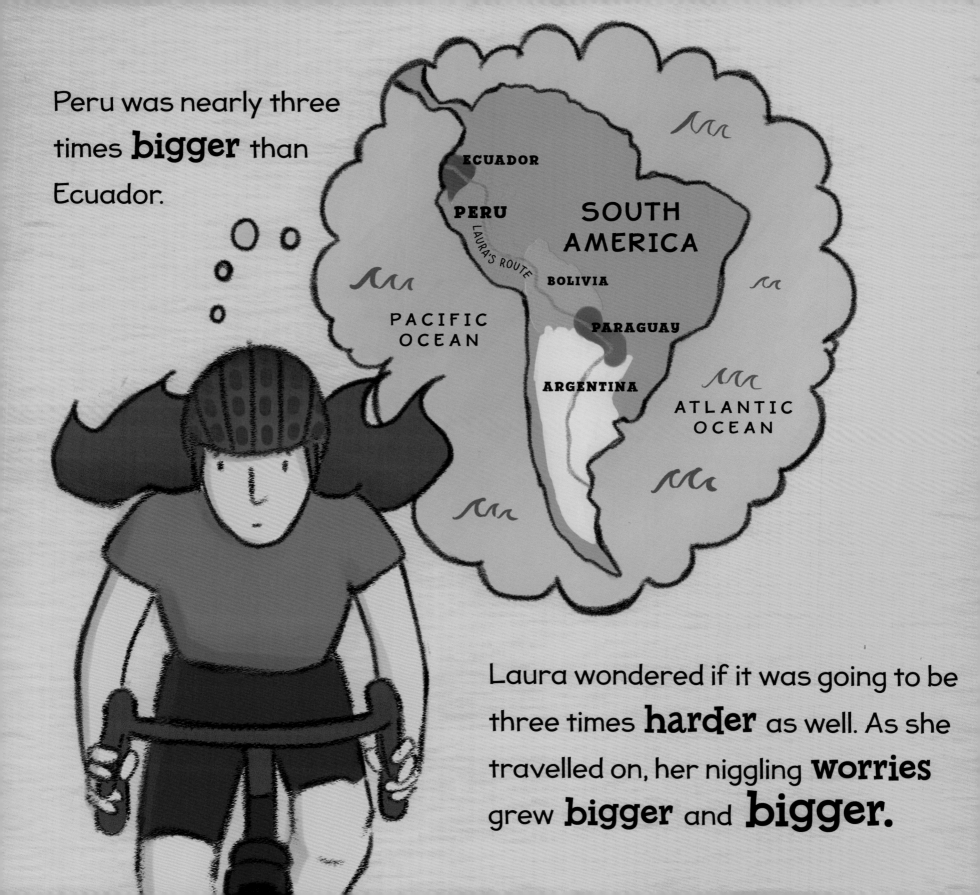

Laura wondered if it was going to be three times **harder** as well. As she travelled on, her niggling **worries** grew **bigger** and **bigger**.

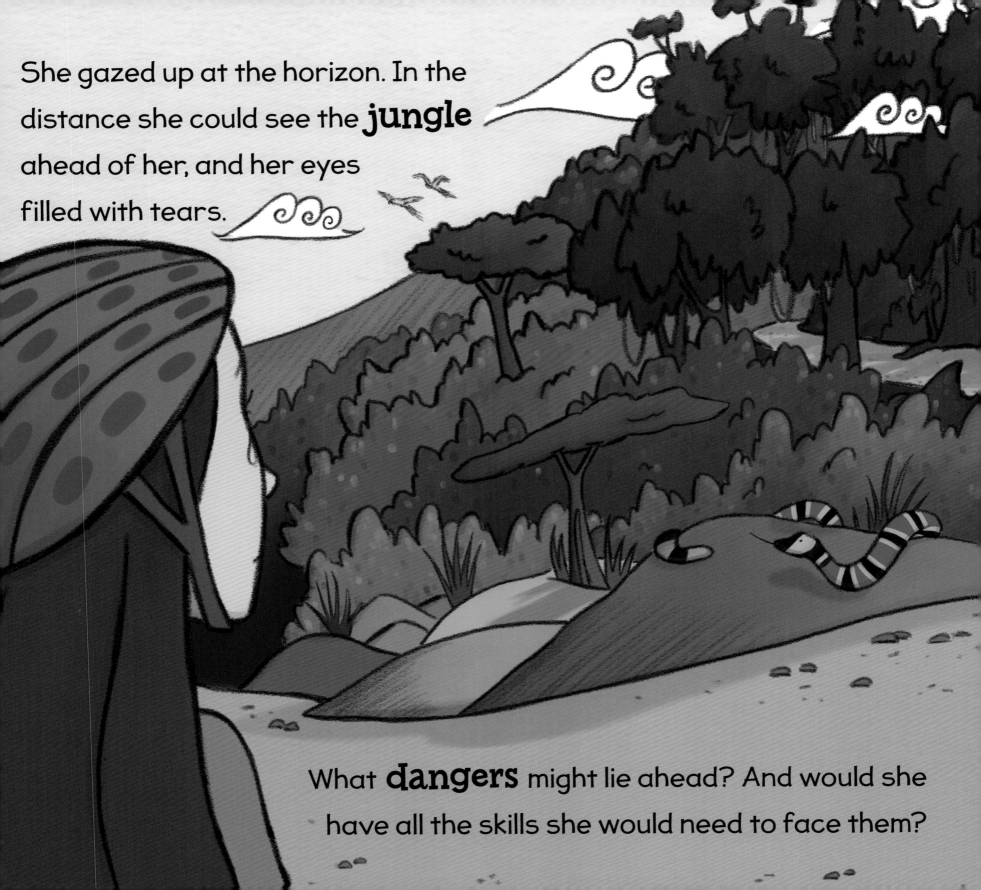

She gazed up at the horizon. In the distance she could see the **jungle** ahead of her, and her eyes filled with tears.

What **dangers** might lie ahead? And would she have all the skills she would need to face them?

With no one to share her joys or her fears, Laura felt very **alone.** A family of odd-looking creatures caught her eye. She stopped to watch them as they played **together.**

And in that moment, Laura knew that she didn't want to ride on her own any more. But she also knew that she wasn't about to give up.

As she began to pedal again, Laura wondered what she could **do** about the loneliness she felt.

Then, **all of a sudden,** the answer came to her.

She needed someone to join her on her journey! But **who** could she ask? And **how** could she contact them?

In a flash, she thought of her friend **Ed.** He loved **adventure** – and he knew how to **survive** in the jungle!

A kind lady let Laura use her phone.

Ed was very **excited** by the thought of a new adventure, and plans were quickly made for him to join Laura in **Peru.**

With Ed now riding beside her, together they admired the **enormous trees** that created welcome shade on the road.

Laura was so happy now that she had **company.** For the first time, her journey felt less daunting, and she began to **laugh** out loud.

As if sharing her **joy,** a red howler monkey called out to them from the treetops.

As they rode on, Ed suddenly started to slow down. "I think there's something **wrong** with my bike!"

Laura stopped and checked it.

"Don't worry, it's just a flat tyre."

She knew exactly what to do.

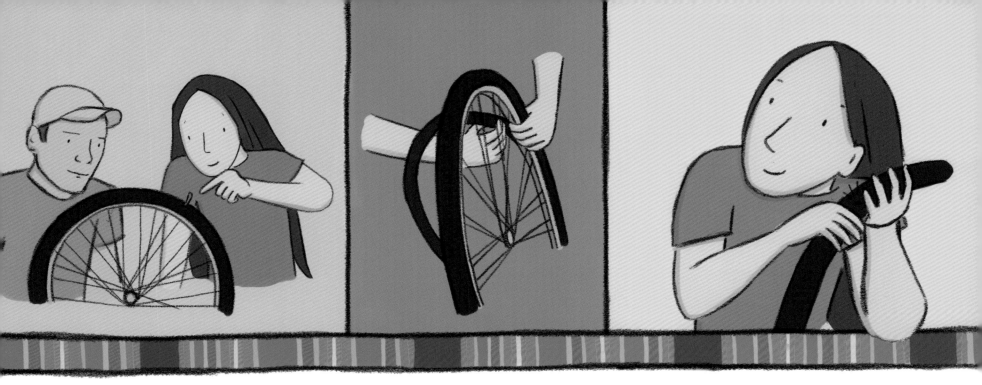

They pulled over to the side of the road so that Laura could mend the puncture. At every step, she **explained** what she was doing and why, so that Ed would know how to fix it next time.

Soon after they set off again, Ed turned to Laura and asked if she had some food. Cycling was **hard work!** But Laura only had a **tiny** amount of rice left.

"Oh," sighed Ed. "Not to worry! I can **teach** you how to forage – to find food from nature."

Laura was thrilled. She loved learning **new skills.** She knew that foraging would be important if she was going to complete her journey without using money.

Leaving their bikes behind, they stepped into the **jungle.**

Suddenly, everything came **alive!** Colours looked **brighter** and sounds seemed **louder.**

Ahead of them, they saw a pair of beautiful parrots **swoop** and **glide,** lifting Laura's spirits as they flew high up into the canopy.

Laura's senses **tingled,** and her whole body seemed to **hum** in tune with the vibrant new world around her.

Ed crouched down and called Laura over.

"That's a leafcutter ants' nest!" he said excitedly. "We can eat the **ants** and the **eggs.**" Laura was not so sure about Ed's choice of meal!

Then Ed pointed up at some fruit that looked like big, lumpy limes.

He picked one from the tree.

"They're guavas," he explained, cutting it open to show her the pink, **juicy** flesh inside. Laura's mouth began to water.

Laura was **fascinated** by everything she saw.
Some enormous ants caught her eye,
and she reached out towards
them in **wonder.**

"STOP!" shouted Ed. "Don't touch them! Those are **bullet ants.** If they bite you, it's as painful as a scorpion sting!"

It seemed there was still a lot to learn.

With their food bags **filled,** and the sounds of the jungle fading behind them, Ed and Laura pedalled on, full of **enthusiasm** for their journey.

Town after town.

Night after night.

Until...

Laura **leapt** from her bike. "Ed? Ed!" she cried as she ran to where he lay in the road. She was so worried. Was he **hurt?** Or **worse?**

She daren't think about that...

"I'm ... I'm OK," he groaned, "but my leg really hurts."

Thankfully, Ed's **helmet** had **protected** his head, but it was clear he wouldn't be able to ride any further. He would have to **fly home.**

But Laura was more **determined** than ever not to give up! So she continued on alone through Peru. Though Ed was no longer with her, she realised he had taught her some **valuable new skills.**

Skills she would use often.

Sometimes **successfully ...**

... and sometimes not!

Though Laura tried to **focus** on the road ahead, her thoughts kept returning to Ed and his injuries.

A loud **squawk** interrupted her worrying. Two macaws flapped noisily overhead, and she knew then that he would want her to put aside her worries and **continue.**

As she cycled on towards Bolivia, Laura wondered what she would encounter in the next stage of her journey, and hoped that perhaps another **friend** might join her.

Peru "Navigating my worries!"

Me!

After the excitement of the early part of my journey, the scale of the trip really began to sink in as I travelled into Peru. I began to worry about everything!

I was still determined to complete the challenge, and raise as much money as I could for Operation South America, but I realised I would have to learn new skills to make myself more self-reliant.

Peru's cloud forests were an amazing sight!

Ed and me – on the journey together

I also knew that I needed to tackle the loneliness I felt. Travelling alone offers a lot of freedom, but when worry and anxiety set in, it's better to find someone to talk to than to have to keep everything to yourself! I was so lucky to have Ed join me, and to have the chance to share part of my journey with a friend.

So, that was the second leg of my adventure completed! It took me 72 days to cycle the length of Peru, a total of 3,055 km.

Sharing skills and finding solutions

We can't all be experts at everything, and just like Laura and Ed, sometimes we need help to improve or learn new skills. Asking for help when you need it is a real strength – especially for an adventurer!

What skill would you like to learn or improve?

Who could you ask to help you?

How long might it take?

How do you think you will feel when you've mastered it?

"If something is wrong, fix it if you can.
But train yourself not to worry.
Worry never fixes anything."
Ernest Hemingway

Did you spot these animals in the story?

Spectacled bear

The only bear species that is native to South America, the spectacled bear is incredibly shy but also very patient – they have been known to sit for days in a tree waiting for fruit to ripen!

Venezuelan red howler

Howler monkeys are some of the largest monkeys in Central and South America. They rarely come down to the ground, and use their gripping tail to help them move around high up in the treetops.

Northern viscacha

Viscachas live in groups in rocky, mountainous areas, where it is easy for them to hide from predators. Viscachas look a bit like rabbits, but they are not related, and viscachas have long, bushy tails.

"For my husband, Ed, who motivates me with love and laughter."

LB

ISBN 978-1-78270-378-5

Text and expedition photographs copyright © Laura Bingham
Illustrations copyright © Laura Wall

Photograph of Laura Bingham (p30 tl) by Brandon Giesbrecht
Animal photographs (l–r): Chris Humphries/Shutterstock.com,
Salparadis/Shutterstock.com, Alex Lee (under Creative Commons 2.0)

First published 2019

Published by Award Publications Limited,
The Old Riding School, Welbeck, Worksop, S80 3LR

19 1

Printed in Turkey